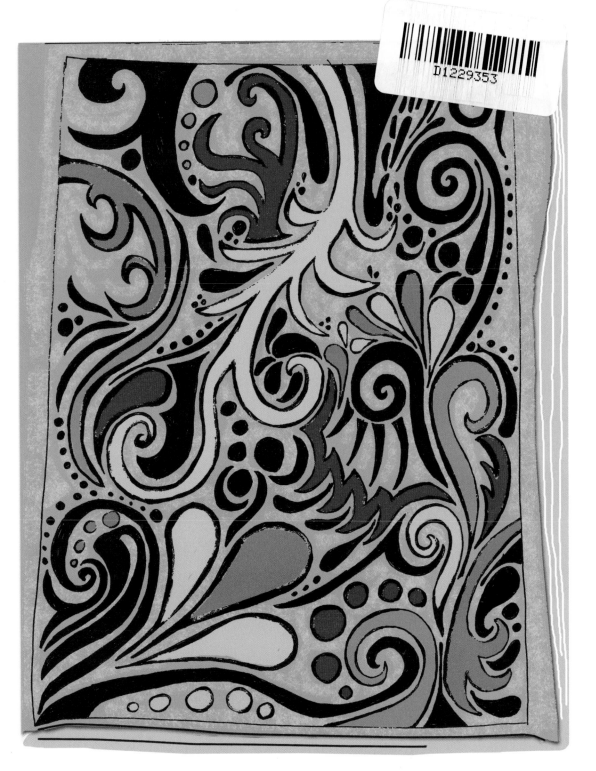

Un.writ.ten Trav.el(s)

by Jenny Black, Jenny Watson and YOU
Doodles by Elizabeth McKnight
Art Design by Don and Chris Wise

Published by
Black Coffee Publishing
P.O. Box 2783
Brentwood, TN 37024
U.S.A.
www.unwrittentravels.com

This publication contains only the opinions and ideas of its authors and
you are to seek your own independent professional counsel or opinion. It
is only intended to provide helpful and informative material on the topics
covered in this book, But you must not rely solely on this information
and perform your own assessment and due diligence, as well as consult
adequate professional counsel. It is sold with the understanding that the
author and publisher are not rendering any services or advice specific to
you. You are required to also consult appropriate professionals on all
matters that require treatment. The author and publisher are not rendering
any professional legal or professional service or advice.

Library of Congress Cataloging-in-Publication Data
Black, Jenny, Watson, Jenny
Black Coffee Publishing
P.O. Box 2783
Brentwood, TN 37024

Printed in the United States of America
ISBN 0-9745238-8-7

1 2 3 4 5 6 7 8 9 10 / 03 01 09

un·writ·ten (un-rit'n) adj.

Not written or recorded: an unwritten agreement between friends.

Having authority based on custom, tradition, or usage rather than documentation: an unwritten law.

Not written on; blank.

trav·el(s) (trav'el)

v.   trav·eled or trav·elled, trav·el·ing or trav·el·ling, trav·els
v.   intr.
To go from one place to another, as on a trip; journey.
To go from place to place as a salesperson or agent.
To be transmitted, as light or sound; move or pass.
To advance or proceed.
To go about in the company of a particular group;
associate: travels in wealthy circles.
To move along a course, as in a groove.
To admit of being transported without loss of quality;
some wines travel poorly.
Informal To move swiftly.
Basketball To walk or run illegally while holding the ball.
v.   tr.
To pass or journey over or through; traverse: travel the
roads of Europe.
n.
The act or process of traveling; movement or passage
from one place to another.
travels. A series of journeys.

An account of one's journeys.

fore.word

As the host of an Internet Radio talk show about making the second half of life better than the first, I encourage women all the time to embrace their deepest passions and birth their best dreams. That requires an awareness of yourself that frankly many have lost...including myself. I've been stuck in my life several times over the years...confused, fearful, and angry at circumstances and people causing change and pain. I've battled depression and still fight against fear, but I desperately want to love others well and live out my calling.

When I started reading **Unwritten Travels** and took the plunge on the inner examination it requires, I began to cry. Lately in all of life's busyness of being a wife, mom of three and having a career, I didn't have much time for inner reflection. I needed a reminder to love myself, to nurture, to proactively bring beauty into my life and to care for my soul. Along came this book at the perfect time and if you've picked it up, maybe it's a good time for you too. Do you want to "understand your story, uncover your passions, your beauty, your value and your purpose?" This workbook will remind you why you need to take care of yourself, how to discover what you were created for and how you can become a "bold life learner".

Unwritten Travels is an invitation to get reacquainted with you! And I love that the authors encourage us to do this and then, not leave our current situations, but engage with and serve our families, our communities, our world as whole women fully alive, freely giving of ourselves, authentically living our lives!

Open your mind and your heart to your possibilities, your desires and your dreams. Discover what brings you joy, what makes you smile from deep within. Take your time with this journey, there's no rush and no pressure.

Debbie Alan

President/Founder of NashvilleNetRadio.com and Host of OnTheHomeStretch.com

Our Traveling Companions
(acknowledgments)

We have shared many seasons of life with the "Bridesmaids." Thank you, Lisa & Lisa, Denise & Denise, Carol, Amy & Cheryl. From you, we learned to journey alongside others, and just as importantly, when and how to be courageous enough to travel solo.

Thank you, Faith, for allowing us to spend time at your cozy cabin on the lake. It is the place where we compiled the first chapter, and organized the format for this book.

Elizabeth, your artwork inspired us on so many levels. We knew we were kindred spirits when we saw your first drawings of girls breaking out of the boxes they were placed in. We still want note cards, business cards and stationery with your doodles on them.

Denise and Amy, you two are real writers. We can't wait for the time when others can purchase your short stories, novels and poems, that until so far, few have had the privilege to experience. You encouraged us to write and were so gentle. You helped us to begin to blossom.

Ann, not only did you edit this book without making us feel ridiculous that we never could spell *souvenir* correctly, your questions helped us to look into our hearts and discover to whom this book was targeted and exactly where we are going.

Thanks to Chris and Don. You are completely responsible for creating a visually pleasing book. Your creativity and enthusiasm are contagious. Thank you for sharing your time and talents with us.

Keoni, thank you for your patience with us during our photo shoot. Your talent worked magic on us that awful winter day.

So many people worked through chapters and gave us feedback along the way. Even though you all were coming from different backgrounds and had different life experiences, you all encouraged us that this book was helpful to you as you navigated life. Thanks to you all: Monique, Janie, Bruce, Angela, Clifton, Kristin, and the many others who have spoken encouraging words and held our hand throughout this journey.

Jenny Black: Adam, you promised in our wedding vows to not only love, honor and cherish me, but to do whatever it took to make my dreams come true. You have been true to your word. Thank you for sharing all of who you are with me.

My kids, Brandon and Avery, you make me laugh every day. You are the best kids a mom could ever have. I love you more than applesauce.

Thank you also to those who have loved and cared for my kids while I was writing: Mindy, Karina, Mrs. Talley, Mrs. Hyrup, Mrs. Pennig, and Mrs. English. Mom, you have taught me everything from how to make tomato soup to how to paint trim. In everything you do, you teach me perseverance and unconditional love.Dad, you continue to teach me to dream big and then you help me reach those dreams. Jerry, you inspire more with your quiet ways than I ever will with all my words. Joy, you are my heart, my hope, my sister, and precious friend.

Jenny Watson: I will never take for granted that I have a husband who is my greatest fan. He encourages me to try anything and thinks my ideas are good. He is my favorite person on the earth. Thank you, Steve, for all your support and unconditional love.

Our children are the greatest blessings for us. They also have encouraged me to pursue any dream I have. They are pursuing their dreams without taking the easy or safe way out. What examples they are to me.

Levi, you have taught me to live my life motivated by things other than obligation. You are so responsible, because your heart is in line with your values. When you do the things you love, you are fulfilling your obligations, and you have fun doing it. I'm still learning from your example.

Lindsey, your life teaches me to be faithful to what I've been called to do. You already know yourself and are true to who you are. You are willing to make the best choices even if they aren't the most popular. I tried to remember to make my choices like this as we completed this book.

Logan, I listen to the voices that say, "Why do you think you can do anything?" If you've ever heard these voices, I know that you answer back, "Why in the world would I not be able?" Then you do it. You give it your all until you excel at it. When I start to doubt myself, I choose to use you to mentor me into believing I can.

Lily, you are the actual motivation behind this book. You have such great ideas. I can't wait to write "our book" together. You were the very first person who believed I could really do something like this. Just in case you aren't sure, I believe you can do anything. I can't wait to see all the adventures you have in life.

There is no way to elaborate on how my extended family has inspired me over the years, so I'll say thanks to them all here: Mom, Dad, Janet, Curt, & Angela, Angie, Lee, John, Susan & Pat, Sheryl & Gary, Sandra & Larry, and the Galloway clan.

Thanks also to the Merry Mary Makers who have walked beside me over the years it took to complete this: Karen, Dannette, Donna, Julie, Sarah, Ana, Dee Dee & Jeanna.

Your Map Key

Your Packing List: This list is included in the beginning of each journey. Some items will be actual resources you need to complete the assignments; others will be internal resources important for your trip.

Road Trip: When you see this symbol, you know you are about to complete a lesson outside of these pages.

Souvenirs: Key items that we have learned from each journey. You will have a place to keep your personal souvenirs.

Creative Excursions: In each chapter a page or two exists for no other reason than to get your creative juices flowing.

Definitions: You may be wondering why we bother to define all of these words. It is important to examine our lives in the same way we have interpreted these words, with a fresh and deeper look into the meaning of our travels.

A *vade mecum* is a term for something carried around by a person for constant use, a reference such a handbook or manual.
It is our hope that *Unwritten Travels*
will become your personal *vade mecum*.

Your Itinerary

Meet your personal *Tour Guides.* / The Story Behind

1. The Honeymoon: discovering your heart's desire

"Being solitary is being alone well: being alone luxuriously
immersed in doings of your own choice, aware of the fullness of
your own presence rather than of the absence of others
because solitude is an achievement." ~Alice Koller

2. Sightseeing: taking a fresh look at your life

Page 32

"Remember, we all stumble, every one of us. That's why
it's a comfort to go hand in hand." ~Emily Kimbrough

3. Soul-Searching: awakening your spirit

Page 72

"All men should strive to learn before they die, what they are
running from, and to, and why." ~James Thurber

4. Your Travel Guide: following your compass

Page 106

"Nobody can be exactly like me.
Sometimes even I have trouble doing it." ~Carl Rogers

5. A Walk down Memory Lane: embracing your past

Page 130

"I've never tried to block out the memories of the past, even though
some are painful. I don't understand people who hide from their
past. Everything you live through helps to make you the person
you are now." ~Sophia Loren

6. Coming Home: living beyond yourself

Page 148

"The value of identity, of course, is that so often with it
comes purpose." ~Richard Grant

Meet your personal *Tour Guides*...

Our first name is not the only thing we share. Both of us are firstborn children. We fit the stereotype of "the oldest," and as a result we were motivated by the desire to please. We made the choices that we thought others expected us to make. We were looking for approval outside ourselves to guide us. These were self-inflicted standards. Our families encouraged "dream following." But while we could applaud everyone else in their pursuits, our own dreams were unknown to us.

While working at a church together, trying to be "good girls," we shared an experience that challenged one of our core beliefs. A belief that we didn't even know we had~ that if we did all the "right things," everyone would be pleased with us. Out of that experience we began the inward journey of discovering who we really are, what we truly believe, and how this knowledge guides us through our daily lives and our relationships with those around us.

Jenny Black: Fourteen years ago, I married my high school sweetheart. Not long after we graduated from college, we had our two children. I was a firm believer in "Happily Ever After", but the deeper belief was that my roles as a wife and a mom would fulfill me and that I would feel valuable as a result. This was too much pressure for all of us! Only when I started to understand what truly makes me valuable (hint: it has nothing to do with roles) did I really begin to enjoy my family. I let the dishes pile up every once in a while and began to take responsibility for my own happiness. Because my kids are still young, I have to be very practical and take baby steps toward my goals and dreams. Today, I am working toward a Master's Degree. Now, instead of being motivated by pleasing others, I am deeply pleased with the opportunity to motivate other women to live passionate and purposeful lives.

Jenny Watson: One day I realized that when I laid my head down at night, I would go through a mental checklist. Laundry done~check! Kids fed~check! Called my mom~check! I was going through the motions of living, but not experiencing joyful life. I thought I was being a good example to my family by focusing on serving my husband and our four children. One evening around the dinner table with my family, we were talking about our favorite foods. I told my kids that my favorite food used to be meat loaf. They were surprised because in 25 years of marriage, I had never made meat loaf. In fact, even I had forgotten that I liked it. As my children are becoming independent adults, I am beginning this unwritten season of my life by rediscovering some joys I had lost along the way. One way I am doing this is by trying all kinds of meat-loaf recipes. Everyone is enjoying the process of discovery, and the lesson is rubbing off on those around me. One discovery I have made is that I can love and serve others while still holding on to the things that make me unique.

The Story Behind
Un.writ.ten Tra.vel(s):

It all started with a plan to meet together once a week and work on one of the many ideas we have talked about over the years. We never imagined ourselves writing or publishing a book. In fact, we consider ourselves to be typical women,

moms and wives

who are doing the best we can most of the time. We are not professional writers, paticularly savvy home organizers, or learned theologians. There are many books on each of these topics (and we have probably read them) that are more in-depth and complete than the book you hold in your hands. We don't have the time to be experts in every area of life, and our guess is that you don't have the time either. We do, however, desire to be an expert on who we are. Our goal is to be fulfilled in our days, and ultimately, our lives. For us, the essential ingredients of a good life include: some level of organization, a splash of pure frivolous fun, a deep connection to our spirits, and an appreciation for family and friends. We have structured this journal so that you can use it even if you only have a few minutes at at time. And, if you are anything like us, that is all you have.

As far as the spiritual aspect of this book: Although we have dedicated one chapter to spirituality, it is our personal belief that God is the beginning, middle, and end of the heart-breaking moments, the heart-warming moments and every boring moment in between. We are writing the book that we wish we could have found when we were looking up and down the self-help aisle for some sort of assistance that was neither "new age," nor non-applicable, rote Sunday-school answers.

We are continually amazed at the ways God shows up for people. It is incredible to see how one person may need God to be a Father, another may need Him to be a Lover, a Comforter, or a Judge. And, how in His omniscience, He can be all of those things at the same time and still meet the deep intimate needs of each individual who longs for Him. Maybe your faith has never wavered. Maybe, like us, you have been disappointed in your spiritual life, and you need God to show up for you in a completely new way. Maybe you don't even know if you believe in God. You may have heard the phrase, "Don't put God in a box." The box is all we know. The box is the the life we are born into and the ways God shows up for us. Because we know that your understanding and experience with God is unique to your life story, we have intentionally avoided any language in our book that would define God for *you*.

This book is dedicated to you. The pages in this book are only a backdrop to your invaluable story. We give you permission to mark up this book and create something truly beautiful with your own story. We hope you have as much fun playing in this book as we have had creating it.

Chapter One

The Honeymoon

discovering your heart's desires

honeymoon

noun, verb.

noun   **1a.** a vacation spent together by a newly married couple:

ex. romantic hand-holding breakfasts together on their honeymoon.

b. (often as adj.) figurative
an initial period of enthusiasm or good-will, typically at the start of a new job: the honeymoon period.

verb   **1a.** spend a honeymoon:
ex. they are honeymooning in the south of France.

Historically,

a honeymoon

is a holiday shared by a newly married couple for the purposes
of bonding before they enter society as man and wife.
We chose to begin our travels with a personal honeymoon, one
you take alone. This is a time to connect you with who you are,
before you enter all of the expectations of real life.

It is easy to lose yourself in your roles as wife, sister, mom,
daughter, employee and/or volunteer. Taking care of yourself
is essential, especially if others are depending on you.
Being alone is the beginning of understanding what you need.
A warm bubble bath and a good night's sleep will not solve all
of the world's problems, but it will give you a better perspective of who you are as you set out on your journey.

Most of us overachieving women know all of the things we
need to be doing better, but we don't often concentrate on
why it is great to be exactly WHO we are right now.
This is the purpose of the Honeymoon...

This is a time to discover what you love, what makes you smile,
and to carry those heart desires into the rest of your journey.

Packing List (for The Honeymoon)

1. Camera — to document your life

2. Flashlight — to enlighten yourself
   (illuminate)

3. Jammies + Slippers (or Super soft socks) —
   for comfort, of course

4. Treats — all natural granola (Naked)
   scented candles (fresh linen),
   your favorite author's newest
   novel, Chocolate (yum!)

5. Music — cds/ iPod, ear buds

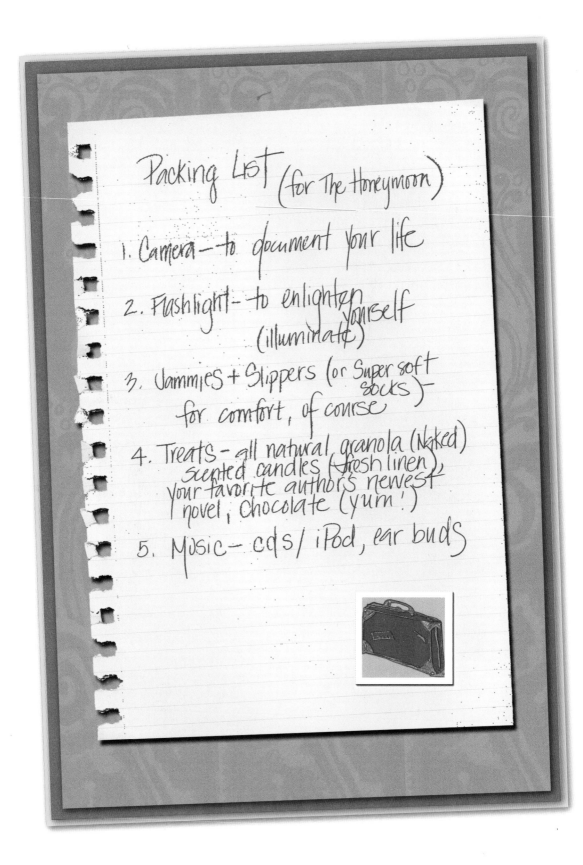

We begin the first pages of

with a simple fill-in-the-blank form.
Use these answers to personalize yourself
and your surroundings as you travel.

The things you love say something about you... listen.

These are a Few of my Favorite Things

"The way to love life ...

color:_____

article of clothing:_____

holiday:_____

movie:_____

beverage:_____

sport:_____

smell:_____

comfort food:_____

snack:_____

magazine:_____

cartoon:_____

T. V. show:_____

restaurant:_____

day of the week:_____

breakfast:_____

song:_____

month of the year:_____

book:_____

"is to love many things"
VAN GOGH

dress:_____

         lipstick:_____

piece of art:_____

         State:_____

perfume:_____

         place to visit:_____

place to live:_____

         flavor:_____

hair color:_____

         shoes:_____

pen:_____

         store:_____

car:_____

         purchase:_____

gift given:_____

         gift received:_____

lingerie:_____

         season:_____

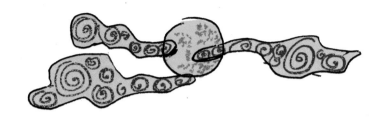

Breathing Room

Once in a while, ideally once a day, you need to be alone.
This may be something you already value.
Do you have a place for personal space?

It is time to create some space just for you.

Think of this place as your Honeymoon Suite. This spot can
be the place you go when you use this journal. This is where
you can be when you are reading the writings of your favorite
author or becoming an author yourself.

What does this safe haven look like? Do you need sunlight
or candlelight? A chair or a bed? Blankets or a fan? Pictures
of loved ones or paintings? Piles of books and magazines
or nothing but a glass of ice water?

Make your "suite" a place that truly belongs to you.
In our spots, we have our necessities (and treats) at hand.
Here we are ready to dive into our
favorite things or to simply sit and be still.

Take the time to visualize this spot. Does it already exist in
your home?

Describe it. Otherwise,
begin to create your honeymoon suite now.

Cut and Paste from Magazines

Your alone spot could be in a corner, in your car, or even on your bed.

Road Trip:

Make a date with yourself to begin creating your honeymoon suite .
If you already have one, make a date to spend some time there.

When can you spend time each day on your Honeymoon? We find mornings to be the ideal time to "get away." Do you have rituals you look forward to in the mornings or evenings?

Of course, there are nights when you can't even change into PJ's before passing out on any available surface. Sometimes, there are mornings when nothing sounds better than several rounds of slamming the snooze button.

But the thoughts that surface as you wake up set the tone of your day. Think about the potential each day holds.

Pour thankful and grace-filled messages into your dreams each evening, and brighten your mornings with a few of your favorite things.

Describe your first waking moments...

What time do you normally wake up?_____

How do you begin your day?_____

_____

What loveliness can you add to your morning ritual?_____

_____

Some Suggestions

~alone time before the rush

~rise and shine music

~an inspiring quote framed at your bedside
"If Joan of Arc could turn the tide of an entire war before her 18th birthday, you can get out of bed." ~E. Jean Carroll

~special morning beverage

~orange, lemon, grapefruit, or mint soaps to awaken your senses

What is your favorite thing to do right before you go to sleep?

_____

_____

What time do you go to sleep?_____

_____

What can you subtract from your evening ritual?_____

_____

_____

Good Night Graces

~soft, clean sheets

~beautiful or cozy pajamas

~eye pillow

~relaxing lotions of lavender, pachouli,

sandalwood or vanilla

Daytime Pondering

Are you filled with deLiGHt or dread when you think of the day ahead of you? Since implementing loveliness into our days, we've discovered the power of alone time before the demands of life start screaming.

Ask yourself,
"At what point of the day do I need the most energy?"
Schedule some time before your meeting or before the kids get home from school.

Take responsibility for RePLeNiSHiNG YOURSeLf when you know ahead of time that you will need extra resources.

> "Don't put off for tomorrow, what you can do today because if you enjoy it today you can do it again tomorrow."
> James Michener

What is your favorite time of day? _____

_____

When are you most productive?_____

_____

How can you use that time to do something important to you?

_____

_____

"A line is a dot that went for a walk." `Paul Klee

Creative Excursion: Take a doodle break.

"Music is what feelings sound like." ~unknown

As our lives became increasingly demanding, music was one of the little luxuries that fell away. Little did we notice that our feelings were fading along with the music. The louder our homes and cars became, the only sound we fantasized hearing was silence. Only in the past year or two has music found its way back into our daily lives. We exercise to music, we meditate to music, we clean our houses to music and we make dinner to music. Music truly brings a richness to our lives that was missing for several years.

What is your favorite song?

Why does this song mean so much to you?

Does it perfectly describe you or what you hope to be?

Does it define this particular season in your journey?

Write out the lyrics to your favorite song.

"Music washes from the soul
the dust of everyday life." ~Auerbach

14

Your honeymoon is a time for wishes to come true. Close your eyes, take a deep breath, and blow out your candles. Think of all of the things you have wished for in years past.
What do you wish for today? No wishing for more wishes!

If I had three wishes...

1.

2.

3.

"What makes the difference between wishing
and realizing our wishes?
Lots of things, and it make take months or years
for your wish to come true,
but it's far more likely to happen
when you care so much about a wish
that you'll do all you can to make it happen."

~Mr. Rogers

Wishes that have been granted...

Wishes that (thankfully) were not granted...

Wishes yet to come true...

Circle the things you love.
Cross out those you hate.

sunbathing	old friends	the mall
snowmen	new friends	clothes
fireplaces	creative writing	shoes
oceans	policemen	pajamas
poetry	candles	lingerie
bowling	crafts	cars
surprise parties	sewing	television
cherries	swimming	computer
art	water skiing	telephone
history	snow skiing	LISTS
magazines	lakes	telephone conversations
coffee	mountains	diamonds
hot chocolate	driving	facial hair
walks	airplanes	umbrellas
runs	bubble baths	stars
pilates/yoga	steam rooms	chocolate
paper dolls	thank-you notes	cereal
flowers	children	rain
babies	puppies	money
teenagers	cats	amusement parks
organization	old bookstores	the news
school supplies	old people	convertibles
flip flops	new boutiques	comics

Examine what you circled and what you crossed out.
Were there any surprises? Use the words from the previous
page to fill in the blanks and answer the questions below.

Why do you love_____so much?

Why do you love_____ so much?

Why do you love_____ so much?

Why do you hate _____so much?

Why do you hate_____so much?

Fill your life with the things you love.

"Be yourself. No one can ever tell you you're doing it wrong."

~ James Leo Herlihy

Road Trip: Paste a picture of yourself here.

Who do people say you look like?

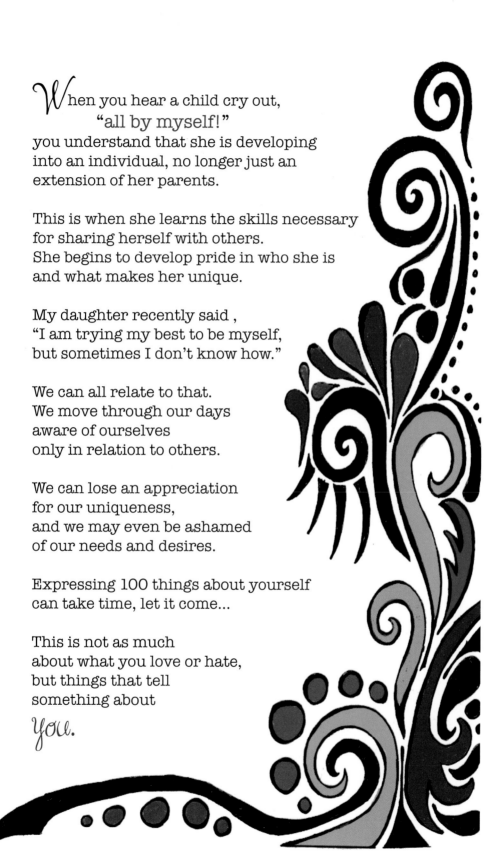

When you hear a child cry out,
"all by myself!"
you understand that she is developing
into an individual, no longer just an
extension of her parents.

This is when she learns the skills necessary
for sharing herself with others.
She begins to develop pride in who she is
and what makes her unique.

My daughter recently said ,
"I am trying my best to be myself,
but sometimes I don't know how."

We can all relate to that.
We move through our days
aware of ourselves
only in relation to others.

We can lose an appreciation
for our uniqueness,
and we may even be ashamed
of our needs and desires.

Expressing 100 things about yourself
can take time, let it come...

This is not as much
about what you love or hate,
but things that tell
something about

you.

100 things . . . .

  1.

. . . . about me.

100.

If I Were a Paper Doll...

Road Trip: Purchase a brand new set of paper dolls.

Play is a child's work. Work like a child today.

Order a catalog from your favorite clothing store and cut
out the clothes you would wear if you were a paper doll.
Paste them here.

Girls *love* Names

We name our dolls, our teddy bears, and even our future children. If you could use any word for your name, what would you pick? Do you have a secret name?

Beloved, Beautiful, Strong, Zany...

Nicknames:

A pet peeve about my name:

Meaning of my given name:

Everyone says I am:

**"Names are not always what they seem.
The common Welsh name Bzjxxllwcp is pronounced
Jackson." - Mark Twain**

My FaVorite Names

Beautiful Dreamer

Has this honeymoon awakened your dreams?
Some dreams stay with us all day. Some dreams answer
questions and others birth new ideas into our lives.

What do your dreams say about you?

Are you a daydreamer?

Are your nights filled with good or bad dreams?

"Dreams are illustrations... from the book your soul is writing about you." ~Marsha Norman

What is the last dream you remember?

What is your favorite daydream?

Did you ever have a reoccurring dream? What was it about?

Road Trip:
Spend some time sky gazing and see what shapes you find in the clouds...

Our Souvenirs

Jenny Black: The Honeymoon Chapter helped me to remember things I love (but had become too "busy" for), like watching cartoons with my kids. I discovered my favorite season is winter because it is the most acceptable season to hibernate. This chapter also revealed to me things I do not enjoy, yet assume I should, like shopping, telephone conversations, and surprise parties. I now realize down time for me is as essential to my well-being as healthy food and fresh air. Being aware of the things I love helps me find a "honeymoon moment" in the midst of getting things done. Now, I don't feel guilty about letting my phone calls go to voice mail while I snuggle with my kids on the couch. At the end of a chaotic day I can, at the very least, say I have taken time, even if it is just a few moments, to enjoy my beautiful life.

Jenny Watson: On this journey, I found I REALLY need to have time alone. I have a husband and four children, not to mention having friends and living close to my family of origin. Was it selfish to desire this time by myself? Initially, guilt set in. The lesson for me is that it is selfish not to do it. I realized something; once you know what you need and who you are, it is up to you to take care of that. Recently, my husband said to me, "When you figure out why you are mad at me, let me know." I knew my snippiness was not his problem. It was mine. As I became aware of the little things I love- flowers, candles, soft sheets, a clean house-I realized how easy it was to incorporate some of these "faves" in my life. The things were probably already there, but the new awareness of them has made me more appreciative, and that feels nice.

Your Souvenirs

~Use what you have learned to make even the most
mundane responsibilities a little bit lovely.
~Believe that your wishes will come true.
~Set aside at least five minutes every day
to do something you love.

Chapter Two

Sightseeing

taking a fresh look at your life

sight

noun, verb.

noun **1a.** the power of seeing; eyesight; vision.
Ex. Birds have better sight than dogs.
b. mental or spiritual vision.
2a. the act or fact of seeing; look.
Ex. One sight of the house was enough to make him want to buy it.
(SYN) glance, gaze.
b. examination; inspection; scrutiny

seeing

conjunction, noun, adjective.

conj. in view of the fact; considering; since.
Ex. Seeing that it is 10 o'clock, we will wait no longer. Deep harm to disobey, seeing obedience is the bond of rule (Tennyson).
(SYN) because.
noun **1.** the act of a person or thing that sees.
Ex. a play worth seeing.
2. ability to see; sight; vision.

You are back from your **Honeymoon**.
You know what you **Love**.
You have learned some things about **Yourself**.

Now, it is time to show up in your own life.

While your honeymoon was to an exotic place- inside yourself-
this next visit is to a place you have been many times before
- ordinary existence.

The

Sightseeing Chapter

is where you will begin to see yourself from a fresh perspective.
When you view your circumstances objectively, you can recognize
your life for what it REALLY is.

On these pages, you will appreciate the richness that already exists in your story. These assignments will also open your mind to
possible solutions for aspects of your "travels"
that you want to improve.

Often, in the routine of living, we lose sight.

Although our lives are full of monotonous tasks much of the time,
a shift in our perspective can bring us to an awareness of how
extraordinary even the ordinary can be.

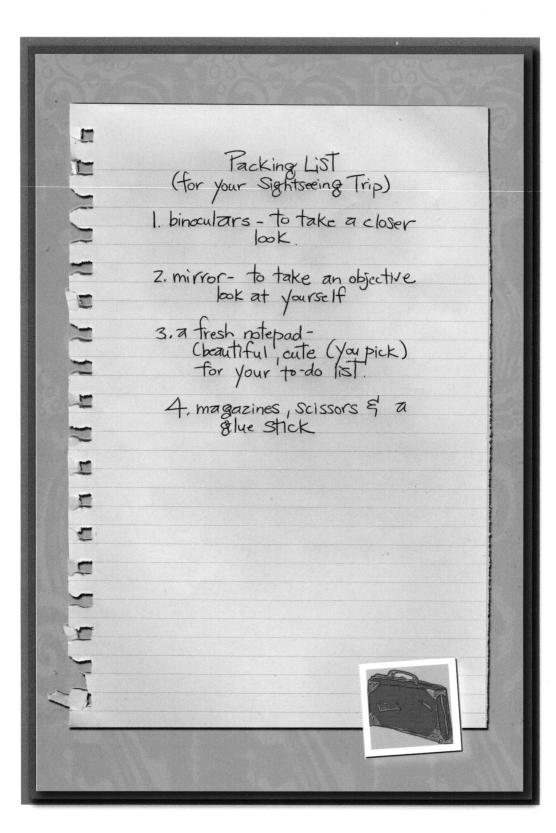

Packing List
(for your Sightseeing Trip)

1. binoculars - to take a closer
   look.

2. mirror - to take an objective
   look at yourself

3. a fresh notepad -
   (beautiful, cute (you pick)
   for your to-do list.

4. magazines, scissors & a
   glue stick

New Eyes

On your Sightseeing Tour, you will take a fresh look at:

Yourself

Your Day

Your Home

Your Friends and Family

It is essential that you view these questions as a caring and non-judgmental friend. Look at your life as an observer. You may even consider asking your close friends: "What do you think of my life?" or "What do you see when you look at me?"

It takes courage to ask these questions, but often, it is only with a fresh perspective that you can see the potential your life holds. You may have lived reactively in the past, but from this point on, you can choose to live intentionally. Moving through your days as a whole person opens your eyes to the lessons your life has to offer.

Take a Good Look

Pretend you are a neighbor just meeting yourself. Hear the knock on the door? Go open it. Whom do you see? Look in the mirror for help with these questions. (P.S. Be gentle.)

How old is she?

What does she look like?

What do you see in her eyes?

How does she carry herself?

What does her expression communicate?

What feature do you love as you look at her?

What feature bothers you?

"Though we travel the world over to find the beautiful, we must carry it with us or we find it not."

~ Ralph Waldo Emerson

Beauty Marks

If your best friend was complaining about her least favorite feature, what would you say to encourage her?

Be your own best friend.

If there is nothing you can do to change your least favorite feature, think of five ways you can begin to accept this attribute. List them.

Does it make you unique?
Do you have the same nose as your favorite grandmother?
Can you see this feature as a connection to her?

1.

2.

3.

4.

5.

Road Trip: Tape this list where you can observe it daily. The next time you feel insecure about this feature, read your list.

an ORDINARY day

Everyone has twenty-four hours each day. Some people thrive on
schedules while others love to take each moment as it comes.
Regardless, at the end of the day, the hours are spent.
Where do your hours go?

What does your typical day look like?

5:00 am	5:00 pm
6:00 am	6:00 pm
7:00 am	7:00 pm
8:00 am	8:00 pm
9:00 am	9:00 pm
10:00 am	10:00 pm
11:00 am	11:00 pm
12:00 pm	12:00 am
1:00 pm	1:00 am
2:00 pm	2:00 am
3:00 pm	3:00 am
4:00 pm	4:00 am

What advice would you give to this person?

How would you evaluate her schedule?

What are you looking forward to?

What are you dreading?

Are you a slave or a philanthropist with your days?

slave, *noun, verb.* **slaved**, **slaving**, *adjective.*
noun **1.** a person who is the property of another. *Ex. We'll visit Caliban, my slave (Shakespeare).*
    2. (Figurative.)
    a. a person who is controlled or ruled by some desire, habit, or influence.
      Ex. A drunkard is a slave of drink. Give me that man that is not passion's slave (Shakespeare).

philanthropist, *noun.*
    a. person who loves mankind and works for its welfare, especially by giving sizable donations of money to worthy causes.
    b. a person who submits to or follows another.

Even if you have a boss who signs your paycheck or children depending on you for survival--you still have a choice to be motivated either as a slave, one controlled by others, or as a philanthropist, giving of yourself. If you feel like a slave to another person, it is possible that you are "ruled" by a perception you have of yourself.

YOU are the only one who has the authority to give someone else power over your life. What voices in your head motivate you to do the things that are on your schedule? Assess whether what you are doing is done because of your own convictions or as a result of your need to meet someone else's expectation of you.

What areas of your day do you have authority over?

Is someone else in charge of any area of your day? If so, who?

Time-Eaters

Think of your time as a resource. In what ways do your opportunities and responsibilities exceed your resource of time? Since more hours cannot be added to your day, take a moment to consider how you may maximize your time for joy and fulfillment.

Identify your greatest "Time-Eaters." These originate from two sources:
*Self-Generated - Disorganization, procrastination, perfectionism, inability to say "no," gossip, etc.
*Environmental - Visitors, phone calls, junk mail, waiting on others, etc.

Self-Generated	Environmental

YOUR THREE most serious time-eaters
and possible ways to reduce their IMPACT:

1

2

3

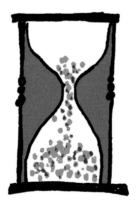

"Dost thou love life? Then do not squander time,
for that is the stuff life is made of."
~ Benjamin Franklin

In the Honeymoon chapter,
we fantasized about some blissful alone time.
In this chapter, we broaden our sights.

How would you spend an
ENTIRE DAY
if you could do whatever you wanted?

An EXTRAORDINARY Day

What would your dream day look like?

5:00 am	5:00 pm
6:00 am	6:00 pm
7:00 am	7:00 pm
8:00 am	8:00 pm
9:00 am	9:00 pm
10:00 am	10:00 pm
11:00 am	11:00 pm
12:00 pm	12:00 am
1:00 pm	1:00 am
2:00 pm	2:00 am
3:00 pm	3:00 am
4:00 pm	4:00 am

Your Wake-Up Letter

"I stayed in a really old hotel last night.
They sent me a wake-up letter."
~Steven Wright

If you suddenly woke up in your own life, exactly as it is today, how would you see it?

Are you pleased with the life you have made for yourself?

What areas of your life are delightful surprises?

What areas of your life are disappointments?

Does it look like the life you hoped it would be ten years ago?

Is there anything you would immediately change?

We know..it is fun to dream, but you have a life
full of responsibilities.
Your possible day is where your ordinary day and your
perfect day meet. After removing some "time-wasters"
from your life...

What can you include in your day that will help you look forward to
what lies ahead?

Your POSSIBLE day

What could your day look like?

5:00 am	5:00 pm
6:00 am	6:00 pm
7:00 am	7:00 pm
8:00 am	8:00 pm
9:00 am	9:00 pm
10:00 am	10:00 pm
11:00 am	11:00 pm
12:00 pm	12:00 am
1:00 pm	1:00 am
2:00 pm	2:00 am
3:00 pm	3:00 am
4:00 pm	4:00 am

Creative Excursion:
Go buy a fresh box of crayons and COLOR!

MAKING a LIVING
or
MAKING a Life

Do you find `money or time` to be more valuable in your life?

Often we have more of one than the other. Most of us believe we are deficient in both. A journey like this one is designed to whittle away the stuff that fills our life but is meaningless to our purpose.

It often takes getting away, on a honeymoon for instance, to realize what you truly have and what you `genuinely need` .

Even with the best of intentions, your lives can begin running you.
Your days are full of obligations.
At the end of the day, the bills may be paid but are you fully living?

How much does your life cost you? This is not a financial question. Has it cost you your passion, your joy, your hope of `making a difference` in the world? When you catch a glimpse of yourself, do you recognize that woman? Are you proud of her? Is she being true to herself? Do you know her?

"Mystery is at the heart of creativity.
That, and surprise." ~ Julia Cameron

The Must-Have To-Do List

"She loves me. She loves me not."

To-do lists are something you love or you "love not." Even if your list is unwritten, you can be haunted by "the list" in your head. It is a constant reminder of all you have to do and all that is left to be accomplished. We hope to help you fall in love with your daily checklist.

If your brain works like an iPhone, you need not read this information. Our brains do not. Using this type of list has changed our lives. Having a to-do list is not a new concept for most people. What makes this one different? It frees up your brain!

Every time you think of a task that needs to be done, write it down. If there is something that you just get an urge to do, write it down! If you suddenly think of an idea, like a great gift idea for someone, write it down!

Why? While you are working on something, you may be reminded of an un-related item or event. You think you will remember that you need to get toilet paper at the grocery store, so you go back to your original task. Often, when you finish, you can't remember what you were supposed to remember.

As you schedule your day, list some of these tasks. If you have a few unexpected dead minutes, take a look at your list and accomplish something. Who doesn't like crossing things off a list?

The next step is the new step. Every day, turn to the next page in your notepad. On this new page write down each item left undone from the day before. Some items may stay on your list for weeks. Some you may cross off because you decide not to do them. Add new items as they come to mind during the day. You will be surprised how much control you maintain instead of letting details run your life. You will also be amazed at how much you get accomplished and how good it feels!

Road Trip:
Purchase your notepad. Write your first to-do list.

What can you do today on your to-do list to surprise yourself?

Take 30 minutes to rest, read, go on a walk.
Make that doctor's appointment or return that phone call
you keep putting off.

Write about how you feel **after completing one thing on your to-do list.**

What would your day look like if you alternated doing something you loved with something you can't stand doing? Go back and look at the souvenirs you brought home from your honeymoon.

What did you learn **that you loved and wanted more of in your life? Now that you have discovered how you live out your life day to day, have you remembered to include some of those newfound loves in your schedule?**

Set aside some money *even a few dollars* each month--to make some of these things become reality in your life.

List some things you _love_ and how you can include even one a week in your schedule.

1.

2.

3.

4.

4.

5.

6.

7.

8.

9.

10.

List some of the things that you can do " _for free_ " with your current resources.

1.

2.

3.

4.

4.

5.

6.

7.

8.

9.

10.

Circle ways you make life work.

Real life expects so much, regardless of job skills or training. You may have never taken a class on filing medical claims and insurance, but it is something we all have to do.
As you look over the list below, think of what you actually do, not what you were prepared to do to "make a living."

accounting	finance	organizing
administrative	grocery	personal shopper
banking	healthcare	photography
business development	hospitality	real estate
caretaking	housecleaning	research
chauffeur	human resource	restaurant
consultant	insurance	retail
counseling	landscaping/upkeep	sales
customer service	legal	science
design	management	transportation
education	marketing	writing

Road Trip: Choose three areas in which you would like to develop more skills. Check out a book for beginners in these fields.

How do you make your life?

Circle the emotions that best describe the way you go about your life.

Ask those who live with you what they think. Circle his/her answers in a different color. What circumstances set in motion these ways of functioning?

busy	yelling	crude
creative	talking	big
energetic	silent	little
lethargic	listening	risky
scattered	controlled	safe
joyful	dreamily	bored
detached	drearily	beautiful
engaged	logically	happy
deep	angrily	proud
on the surface	frivolously	competitive
peacefully	drained	perfect
rushed	hungry	out of control
task-oriented	weak	plodding
relationship-oriented	strong	steaming
surviving	passionate	fully
fearful	pious	growing

THERE'S NO PLACE LIKE HOME

"If we can only keep together and grow up good, so that the Little
Brown House won't be ashamed of us, that's all I ask."
~Margaret Sidney

Describe your home.

Who...

What...

When...

Where...

Why...

Sight...

Feel...

Taste...

Smell...

Tour of Your Home

Go through each room in your home.
Look at it through the eyes of a prospective buyer.

Entrance

Dining Room

Living Room

Kitchen

Bedrooms

Bathrooms

Family Room

Garage

Front/Back Porch

Front/Backyard

Dreaming of a... Home

What would your dream home look like?
Paste pictures from magazines here.

*What can you do to make your current home
more like your dream home?*

Are there other homes that you like better than yours?

If so, what is it that you like?

Do you have a space that is all your own?
(Go back to "Your Favorite Spot" for inspiration.)

Things you can change about your home...

Things you can learn to accept about your home...

Idea list to change your feelings about your home

- Paint a room.
- Rearrange the furniture.
- Clean out and organize the closet or the drawers in one room.
- Change the use of a room to meet some of the needs of the people who live here.
- Hire a cleaning person to get everything cleaned at once.
- Buy your favorite flowers.
- Find a scent you love and buy candles with that scent.

Your Ideas	Steps to Take	Due Date
1.		
2.		
3.		
4.		
5.		
6.		
7.		
8.		
9.		
10.		
11.		
12.		

Picking one idea to work on each month--
you will have all of these things done in one year!

SHARED SPACE

"Deep listening is miraculous for both listener and speaker. When someone receives us with open-hearted, non-judging, intensely interested listening, our spirits expand."
~Sue Patton Thoele

Who lives with you/works with you/hangs out with you?

1.

2.

3.

4.

5.

Be intentional about making eye contact with these individuals and ask, "Is there anything you want to share with me?"
List some of the things you discover.

Road Trip: Do not continue on to the next page until you have completed one listening assignment.

HOUSEGUESTS

We have had the opportunity to have various people live in our home for different periods of time. Some were in transition between homes of their own and only stayed for a month or two. Some stayed for up to a year. It taught our family a lot about ourselves. Think about your household.

If someone came to live in your home, what would change?

What do you think that your guest would list as your family's strengths and weaknesses?

How would you treat each other differently?

How can you use your thoughts to make your household better?

Ways to enjoy your Family

Have a book group together.

Play a board game.

Do a puzzle.

Go to a bookstore together.

Window-shop at a toy store.

Have one family member's friend(s) over and hang out together.

Go bowling, to a movie, or to play miniature golf.

Compile a family tree and discuss with younger generations what you know about the older generations.

Allow each person to plan the menus on certain nights.

Write notes telling each other what you appreciate about one another.

Make a family CD. Allow each person to pick two songs for the CD.

Volunteer together in the church nursery, at a homeless shelter, or helping a sick neighbor.

Ask questions to get to know each other better.
        (Use the favorites page from the Honeymoon chapter.)
Ask "feeling questions" - When have you been scared? What is your greatest fear? Your most embarrassing moment? Your earliest memory? Your proudest moment?

Write a story together. Ask one person to think of the first line. Pass the paper to the next person, who adds a line. Each time you pass the paper to the next person, fold down the pages so that only the previous sentence can be seen. After everyone has had a turn, unfold the page and read the whole story.

the CHARACTERS of YOUR STORY

The people who live in your house affect your life in every way. Your friends, those with whom you CHOOSE to share life, can have just as great an impact.

Pretend that you are describing OLD FRIENDS to a new friend. In your description, think about their interests, their sense of humor, the way they relate to others, the way they make you feel being with them.

REFLECT - What do you learn from taking an objective look at your friends? Who do you want to be around more? Who can you learn from? Who stimulates you to grow as a person, and how do they do that? Who do you need to encourage? What strengths do they have that you want to develop? What challenges do they have that you want to avoid?

My Friend, _____

My Friend, _____

My Friend, _____

My Friend, _____

"Friend. Good." - Frankenstein

In Case of Emergency, Call...

The friend who always makes me laugh is _____

The friend who laughs at my jokes is _____

The friend who cries with me is _____

The friend who confronts me is _____

The friend who always believes that I am better than I think I am is _____

_____

The friend who is always up for something fun is_____

The friend who stands beside me is _____

My most interesting friend is _____

The friend that is the most fun to share dreams with is _____

The best listener I know is _____

Now you have taken inventory of your friendship resources. When you are looking for a certain service, you consult the phone book to find someone who meets that specific need. This is your personal directory for when you need a friend.

Email your friends to tell them what you appreciate about his or her friendship.

"Let us be grateful to people who make us happy;
they are the charming gardeners who make our souls blossom."
- Marcel Proust

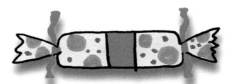

With whom do you spend most of your time?

How do your friends add to your life?

How do they take away from your life?

Who is your oldest friend?

Who is your newest friend or acquaintance with potential?

Ways to meet new friends:
* Pursue a hobby. * Start going to a gym. * Take a class. * Invite neighbors over for dessert or to watch a special event. * Volunteer. * Ask someone to help you with a project. *

Pace Yourself

*Are you ready to slow down
and enjoy your life and the people in it?*

What do you worry would happen if you paused?

We all have too many balls in the air...juggling our way through
our days...running from the voices that tell us we are failing and
toward the cheers that praise our daily efforts.
These voices can become so loud that we may not hear a friend
who is hurting, or a child who does not feel accepted.
We may not even recognize our own voice.
Take a sick day before your body has to take one for you.

Gratitude

"GRATITUDE unlocks the fullness of life. It turns what we have into enough, and more. It turns denial into acceptance, chaos to order, confusion to clarity. It can turn a meal into a feast, a house into a home, a stranger into a friend. GRATITUDE makes sense of our past, brings peace for today, and creates a vision for tomorrow." ~Melody Beattie

**After going on this Sightseeing Trip,
what are you grateful about:**

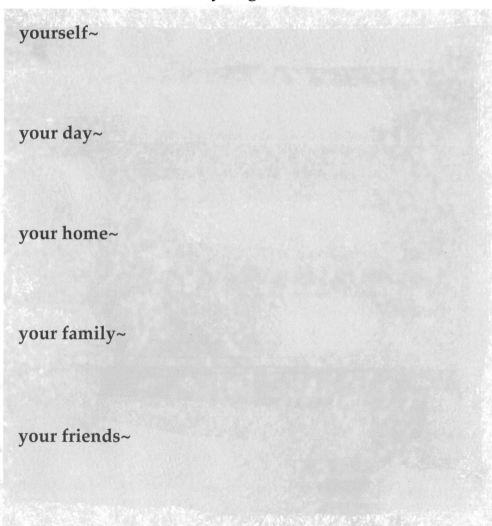

yourself~

your day~

your home~

your family~

your friends~

Our Souvenirs

Jenny Black: My library shelves are lined with every home/family/life organization book on the market. Despite all of my attempts to get organized, I remain a mess. Having a neat and clean house where I can always find what I need, has always been one of my top priorities... and one that eludes me. I used to get so frustrated with myself when we would run out of toilet paper or have nothing defrosted for dinner. One day, my (amazingly organized and disciplined) husband told me, "If I were the one at home with the kids all day, our house would be in order, but our family would be a mess. You may not be able to keep the house together perfectly, but you keep our family happy." Although I deeply appreciate the grace my family gives me (and all the ways they work to help our daily life happen), real life requires me to be disciplined in areas that do not come naturally for me. I am so thankful for all of those organized women who wrote great books to help me keep my sink shiny, my life simple, and my family sane.

Jenny Watson: When I think of my life, I think of it as typical. Then, I will see a television program about someone meeting her biological parent for the first time at age 18, and I'll think, "Oh, I've done that." A new book will come out about losing a parent to cancer; I've done that too. Being married for 25 years is something that some would consider extraordinary. I've run a marathon. I've had four children in less than six years, and raised them into the teens and early adulthood. I've had a dad who got married less than a year after my mom died (to someone he had dated for six weeks) and a biological dad who has been married four times. Taking a look at my life as if I were an outsider revealed to me that I've lived through some things. As I introduced myself to myself on this journey, awareness grew that this girl can handle stuff. It explains why moving two kids into college this fall seems like "no big deal." BUT just because I can handle things doesn't mean I have to do it all by myself. That's what friends are for, and I need them more than I have realized. The souvenirs from this chapter are more numerous than I can share here. They will not be put away in a box in my closet like the shells I brought home from the beach. They will impact my life. I'm determined to learn from them and use them.

Your Souvenirs

~Be gracious to yourself. Appreciate how hard you work.
You really ARE amazing!

~Don't be afraid to acknowledge areas in need of improvement.
Even small steps will move you toward health. Perfection is not the goal.

~Nurture those relationships that nurture you.

Chapter Three

Soul~Searching

awakening your spirit

soul

noun, adjective.

noun   1. the part of the human being that thinks, feels, and makes the body act; the spiritual part of a person as distinct from the physical.

Many religions believe that in death the soul and the body are separated and that the soul lives forever.

2. energy or power of mind or feelings; spirit; fervor. (SYN) heart.

3. (Figurative.) the cause of inspiration and energy; leading spirit; prime mover.

4. (Figurative.) the essential part (SYN) essence, substance.

5. a person; individual.

6. Soul, God.

7. the quality that stirs emotion or sentiment, especially in a distinctive spirit of African culture.

searching

adjective.

1. examining carefully; thorough.
2. keenly observant; penetrating.
3. piercing; sharp; keen.

After our Sightseeing venture, hopefully you have come to a clearer understanding of the life you are really living.

This next chapter will investigate an area of your life that many times is ignored. This may or may not be intentional. If you continue to neglect a whole part of who you are then you will never come to a place of genuine balance.

~When was the last time you thought about your soul?
~How is it doing? Is it thriving? Is it tired?
~Do you even believe you have soul?

As we complete the Soul-Searching chapter, we will personally and intimately interact with our souls.
You may be meeting yours for the first time.

In
Soul-Searching

you will uncover:

*How to find rest in the deepest places of your soul.

*How to get to a place of silence in your minds, so that you can begin to really hear.

*What you (really) believe about the Creator of your soul.

*The promises that are written on your heart.

If you are a woman who has been disillusioned and disappointed by your faith, you may feel hesitant to go through this chapter, even dreading it.
We trust that you have the courage to open your heart one more time.

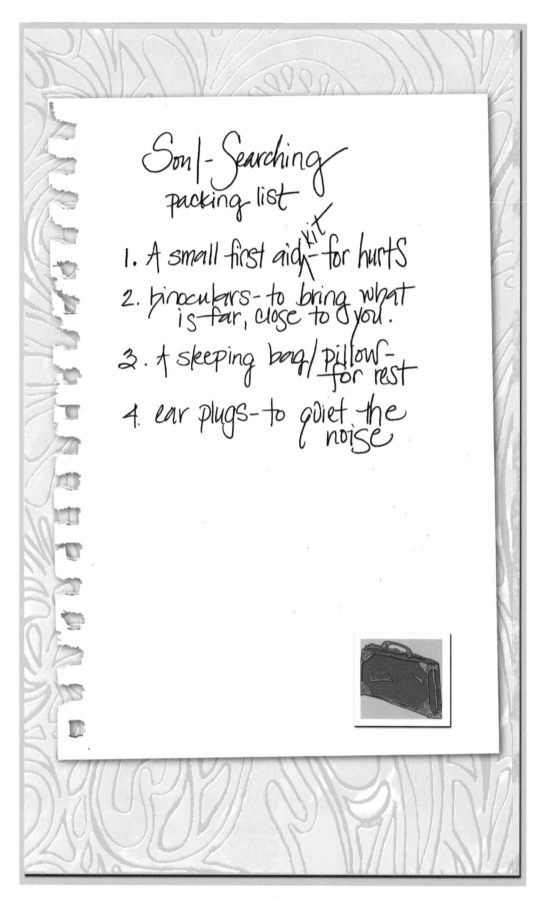

Soul-Searching
packing list

1. A small first aid kit - for hurts

2. binoculars - to bring what
   is far, close to you.

3. A sleeping bag/pillow -
   for rest

4. ear plugs - to quiet the
   noise

A Moment of Silence

"It is in deep solitude that I find the gentleness with which I can truly love my brothers. The more solitary I am the more affection I have for them.... Solitude and silence teach me to love my brothers for what they are, not for what they say."
~Thomas Merton

You are going to begin this part of your travels with silence.

If there is anything our busy lives truly lack, it is quiet.

Not simply a lack of sound, but a stillness of the mind.

If you really want to hear what is going on in your soul, you must have silence in your life.

Otherwise, you will be listening to voices that are not your own, following paths that were not intended for you, and missing the wholeness you seek.

As you look at the following pages,

~close your eyes.

~clear your mind of all of its clutter.

~breathe~

Take in the *beauty* of <u>nothing</u>.

Leave this page blank.

Open some s p a c e in your life.

Let your soul become LOUDER!

What thoughts surface when you try to clear your mind?

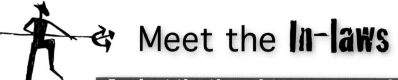

Meet the In-laws

Look at the thoughts you wrote down on the previous page.

You have just been introduced to some of the thoughts that sabotage your quiet mind. I call them them "In-laws"because it is universally acceptable to blame all current problems on the in-laws. When I first started studying family psychology, we turned to the section about in-laws and there was less than a paragraph. In-law issues are not about the in-laws. The issues you have with in-laws (could also be work or friends) are not the root issues, they are echos of the stuff you are struggling with all on your own. Any problem you have that causes you to say,

> "If only this would happen or they would change" is what we refer to as the in-laws.

It would be great if you could simply ignore all of those messages, but you must understand and even appreciate these voices before you can stop listening to them. If you try to pretend they are not there, they will only settle down for a while and then come back more demanding than ever.

Where do your messages fit in the catagories below?

Keeping busy (Write out your bills):

Good (Someone loves me):

Bad (I am not talented):

Guilty (I should be helping Granny):

Shame (I am bad):

De-Cluttering your sacred space

What do you feel guilty about?

What do you blame yourself for?

What are you afraid of?

What is your biggest fear?

Who is someone you are *jealous* of? Why?

What *good* things about yourself do you use to make you feel better about *bad* things in your life?

Who do you *compare* yourself to in order to feel better about yourself?

How do you *justify* choices you make?

What are your *vices*?

What *situations* most often drive you to your vices?

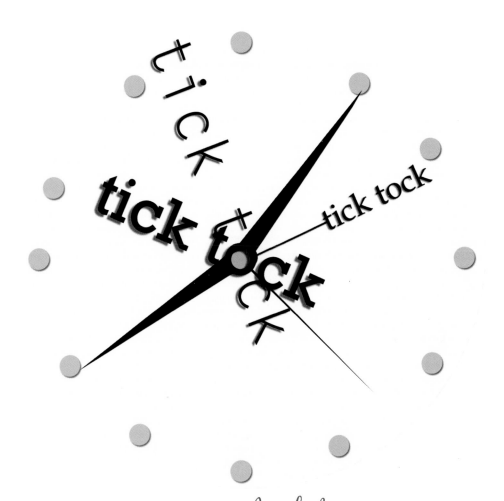

The voices that speak the *loudest* are the ones that
jolt you out of your sleep, or keep you under the covers
(wanting to hide from the world).

Our *Hope* is that you find a quiet, clean space
(underneath the good, the bad, the shame and the guilt)
from which you begin to live.

But you have to be willing to listen...

You may have to practice this exercise many times before
you can stop thinking, but it is worth the wait.
This is not what "should" be in you.
It is allowing the stuff that has been stuffed to surface.
If you want to receive everything life has for you, be open
to thinking, or rather not thinking, in a whole new way.

Write down any new thoughts or voices you heard from your heart as you quieted your mind.

That is what the enemy of your soul would have you believe.
Because silence could begin the richest season in your life.

Some women don't want to be silent
because they are afraid of what they will feel
(and it is usually something they have been avoiding
for a very long time). Others may think if they stop checking off
things on their to-do lists, they will lose their purpose.

This is the time you will find your purpose.
Hear what is going on in your heart.

What *fears* **keep you from being silent?**

What *ambitions* **keep you from being silent?**

Describe a moment that you felt your soul was at *rest.*

When you respond to the good/bad voices in your head,
you give them more power than the promises in your soul.

"A promise is a cloud, fulfillment is rain."
~Arabian Proverb

Awaken that woman inside of you who was born with promise.
You remember her.
You even remember those promises.

All of those voices that describe how you are doing it perfectly
or remind you of your failures are simply a mirage,
clouding the hope that is hidden in your deepest places.
Some of them may seem so crazy, too big...
Who are you to do something that amazing?
Some of them may seem so small,
it is silly to call them a promise,
but hold on to them with all of your heart.

Lovely clouds, it is time to rain.

Your Promise Ring

Rings carry promises with them--

I love you.
I will marry you.
I will take care of you.

An heirloom ring reminds you of the one
who used to wear it
and the family to whom you belong.

What are your promises? Your deepest desires?

The ones you found when the rain washed away
the voices in your head.

Road Trip: Find a ring
(in an old jewelry box or glistening in a jewelry store window).
Wear it to remind you of where you came from,
the promise of where you are going,
and the complete acceptance of who you are today.

"To accomplish great things, we must not only act, but also dream; not only plan, but also believe." ~Anatole France

What are your spiritual beliefs?

What do you need from God? If you are not sure, SEEK.

What is your favorite thing you believe about God?

What bothers you about God?

What do you want to say to God?

Dear God,

Sincerely,

Me

What do you hear God saying to you?

Dear

Love,

God

How would you like to practice what you believe on a daily basis?

Have you had an experience where you felt or knew that something greater than yourself was involved?

Describe your spiritual role model (or what you would like in a spiritual role model).

Which of your beliefs help you?

Which of your beliefs hurt you?

How have your beliefs changed over time?

How have your beliefs about God affected your beliefs about yourself?

"There is a time and a season for everything,
and a season for every activity under Heaven."
~Ecclesiastes 3:1

The journey of awakening your spirit is not one for the timid.
Experiencing life to its fullest is not always a day at the spa.
You will feel some wounds you thought were only scars.
You will find some strengths where you only believed there
were weaknesses. You will hear the truth and the truth will set
you free. Free to be the woman you had only hoped you
were created to be.

The third chapter of Ecclesiastes
is such a beloved passage.
It brings dignity to every emotion
you could ever feel.
You can just hear the author saying,

"This is all life. Accept the process.
This is who you were made to be."

Describe the following times and seasons of your soul.
When were you aware of a birth or death inside of you?
When was the last time you just needed to laugh?
Have you poured years of your life into something that you
knew it was time to tear down?

A time to be born and a time to die...

A time to plant and a time to uproot...

A time to kill and a time to heal...

A time to tear down and a time to build...

A time to weep and a time to laugh...

A time to mourn and a time to dance...

A time to scatter stones and a time to gather them...

A time to embrace and a time to refrain...

A time to search and a time to give up...

A time to tear and a time to mend...

A time to be silent and a time to speak...

A time to love and a time to hate...

A time for war and a time for peace...

"AND YOU WOULD ACCEPT
THE SEASONS OF YOUR HEART
JUST AS YOU HAVE ALWAYS ACCEPTED
THAT SEASONS PASS OVER YOUR FIELDS
AND YOU WOULD WATCH WITH SERENITY
THROUGH THE WINTERS OF YOUR GRIEF."

~ KAHLIL GIBRAN

If you have not experienced some of the seasons,
your time will come. Be on the lookout.

What season are you in right now?

What gifts have you received from some of the more
challenging seasons of your life?

Embrace the season you are in today.
If it is your time to grieve, don't try to rush into laughter.
If it is your season for planting,
do not be frustrated by your lack of results.
Remember, this too will pass, but not until you receive the gift
your season is holding out to you.

Create a collage of the time and season of your life today.

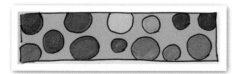

Creative Excursion:
Use magazines, scissors, and glue to create your collage.

When you hurt...

What about the places that ache? Sometimes, those throbbing wounds are so close to the surface you can't breathe. Other times, they are deeper.

What are some painful memories / situations that make you ache?

What things did you begin to believe about yourself as a result of the situation?

What things did you begin to believe about God?

Was this the first time you ever felt this feeling?

If not, when was the first time you felt this ache?
(You might have to spend some time meditating on this.)

What ways do you COPE *when you feel this ache?*

One definition of COPE is to cover, as with a cape.
Our coping mechanisms do not help us
with the recovery of our souls.
In fact, they often separate us farther from feeling
and knowing the promises of our story.

Resilient
or
Silent Soul

Typical responses to hurt:

1. The other person is evil
   ~find others to confirm this belief for us.

2. We believe we are inadequate, failures, etc.
   ~receive all messages that support this belief.

3. We self-talk about how good we are
   -receive all messages that support this belief.

How you respond to hurt
in your life
will determine the person you become.

It is unfair.
We wish you were never hurt.

Some of you
may have been wounded
in violent ways
that we can't even imagine.

Do not hear us
belittling your pain.
We know it is real.

We know that the anger
and bitterness
and ache
are justified.

But we also know you are a Bright and Beautiful Light.

Although you should know and understand the pain,
it cannot not define you.

No woman has a promise of Heartbreak and Bitterness
written on her heart.

Heartbreak and Bitterness silence the Promise.

Do not allow this hurt to be the end of your story.

Even the sweetest, kindest, most pure action can come from and lead to places of anger, manipulation and control. As a human being, each of us has hurt someone else's feelings. Maybe it was unintentional, but we have participated in inflicting wounds on others.

The act of asking others for forgiveness is one of the greatest tools in being able to forgive. When you take responsibility for participation in hurting another, you have a new understanding of grace to forgive those who have hurt you.

Whom have you hurt?

Can you make amends? If not, write a letter. Read it to a close friend.

Allow this act of humility to wash over you.
Forgive yourself. Let it go.

In Chapter One, we asked you some questions about your name. We ask you to look into your soul and find your "secret name" ~ the name that resonates with the promises of your story.

For example, today my name is "beautiful"

Today my name is _____

Yesterday my name was_____

Tomorrow my name will be _____

My friends think my name is_____

The _____think my name is_____

My parents think my name is_____

Secretly I know my name is_____

Our Souvenirs

Jenny Black: I considered myself completely abandoned to God, available to do what He wanted with me. And then I got hurt...really hurt...just trying to please Him. So not only did I begin to protect my heart from potential harm from others, I withdrew my heart from God. I did not trust that God was looking out for me. I felt used up by God. I still believed in God, but I was done with devotions and memory verses, and trying so hard to be godly. I began to look out for myself, learned how to make some healthier choices, set some boundaries, and grew a spine. As I wrote in my journal and went to counseling, I began to see that many of the ways I was attempting to please God were rooted in people-pleasing, insecurity, and guilt. My hurt did not have much to do with God at all. Over a number of years, I reluctantly began opening my heart to God. The God I had been serving and pleasing was really a god of my own making. The God I worship today is One I will never fully understand, but One in whom I have found rest.

Jenny Watson: I became more aware of the voices that are speaking to me all day, especially in the quiet. My personal voices aren't always condemning me or praising me. They seem like innocent daydreaming, but they are attacking my soul. They frame all of my experiences and play them back for me. Unfortunately, the playbacks are mainly of the hurtful experiences, the ones where I feel I was wronged. The voice I hear loudest is one that encourages me to be angry, hurt and negative. On our Sightseeing trip, I realized that I wasn't as negative as I thought. On this journey, I realized that I can absorb the negative voices screaming at me, or I can refuse to listen and allow the positive voice to be heard-not a voice that is praising me, but a voice that is thankful. This voice sees how everything that has happened in my life has taught me, molded me, and allowed me to experience the blessings of forgiveness. I am reminded of an old proverb that says, "Be careful what you think, because your thoughts run your life" (Proverbs 4:23 NCV). My decision is to choose to listen to my soul and believe the dreams that are there for me to receive, and to go forth with joy knowing everything that has happened in my whole life has prepared me to be able to receive.

Your Souvenirs

~ Access to places of rest in your soul
~ Ownership of the promises your life holds
~ Authority to hush voices that steal from you

Chapter Four

Your Travel Guide

following your compass

travel

verb, noun.

v.i. **1.** to go from one place to another; journey.
2. to go from place to place selling things.
3. to move; proceed; pass.
4. to walk or run.

noun **1.** the act or fact of going in trains, ships, cars, and the like, from one place to another; journeying.
2. movement in general.

guide

verb, **guided, guiding,** *noun.*

v.t. **1.** to show the way; lead; direct; conduct.
2. to direct the movement or course of.
3. to direct in any course of action.
4. to manage; control; regulate. (SYN) govern.
v.i. to act as one who guides.
noun **1.** a person or thing that shows the way, leads, conducts, or directs.
2. a part of a machine or device for directing or regulating motion or action.
3. guidebook.
4. guidepost.
5. something which marks a position or serves to guide the eye.
6. a soldier posted at the right or left front of a column when marching, with whom all other members of a unit align.

Before you leave for a vacation, you decide
where you want to go, what you want to see and do,
and how much you want to spend.
You set out on your journey with travel guide in hand.
How many of us take the time to do this for
ourselves?

To live a life that is flourishing, you have to

clarify your life values

and then figure out how to live by them.
You are already living by a set of personal rules.
Most of the time you are unaware of the values that
guide you. Usually they are absorbed from someone
or somewhere else.
You answer yes or no to the questions life presents
to you based on these rules.
Becoming intentional about your values
frees you to live a consistent life,
in harmony with your soul.

Living according to someone else's guide
will leave you frustrated and unfulfilled.
You are the only one who can

create your own travel guide.

In this chapter you will take a look at your

personal compass.

After determining what you value and deciding
if you need to make any changes, you will have
your own personal guide.

This travel guide will not consist of pages in a book
that become worn and tattered;
it will be written in you.

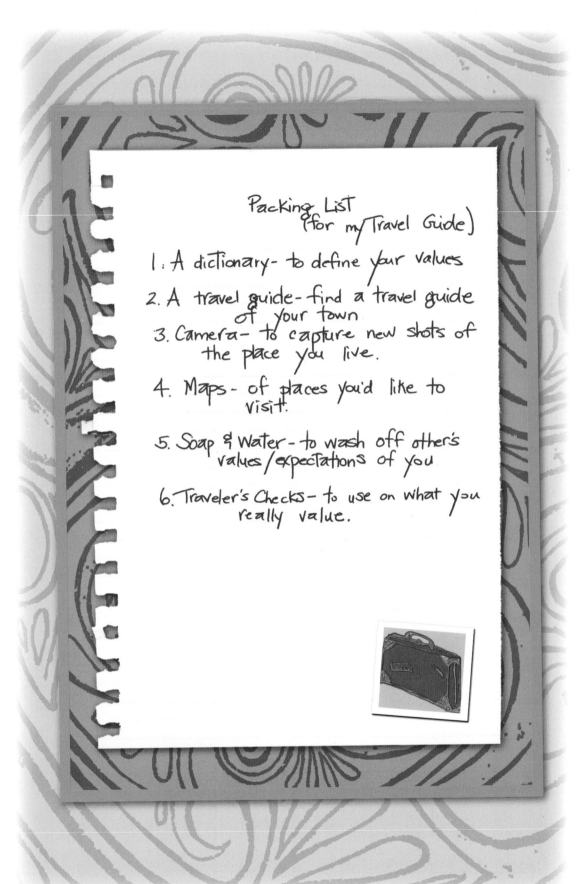

Packing List
(for my Travel Guide)

1. A dictionary- to define your values

2. A travel guide- find a travel guide
of your town

3. Camera- to capture new shots of
the place you live.

4. Maps- of places you'd like to
visit.

5. Soap & Water- to wash off other's
values/expectations of you

6. Traveler's Checks- to use on what you
really value.

Write down what comes to your mind when you ask yourself the following questions:

How would you define something valuable?

What do you value?

What do you think you are supposed to value?

How are your values influenced by your environment?

How are your values influenced by your soul?
(Refer to Soul-Searching.)

You may value your wedding ring, your relationships,
your children, your work or your home.
The following pages will clarify the values that underlie the
reasons why these things are so valuable to you.
Take a look at this list of common values.
Add any values that you listed on the previous page.

What values do you want to embrace?

What values do you want to release?

"Be more concerned with your character than your reputation,
because your character is what you really are, while your reputation
is what others think you are." ~John Wooden

Why is it important to know what you value?

With our need for attention and approval, we typically observe
the standards set by others and then attempt to live up to them.

As you become a fully alive woman, the quieter voices
of what you truly hold dear will begin to surface.

This can be uncomfortable...because the person you have "tried"
to be all of your life is beginning to become her own person.

Will she still be accepted?
Will she be able to live up to her own values?
What if other people are dependent on you to continue acting
on values that you want to give up? This takes courage.

We cannot change other people. We <u>can</u> change ourselves;
therefore our relationships will change.
Some relationships will become more satisfying while others
can become more frustrating.

Do you have some values that exist to please someone else?

Do you have some values that exist in rebellion to someone else?

Rebellion and/or people-pleasing, are both REACTIONS.
To be at a place of peace, our choices must be motivated
by what WE feel/believe;
otherwise, we are allowing ourselves to be controlled.

"If you don't know where you're going, any road will get you there." ~Lewis Carroll

Look at your list and decide which values
are most important to you.
Write them in order of importance.

1.

2.

3.

4.

5.

Are any of your values holding you back?

Jenny Watson: I value order. This can save time. If everything is in its place, then I don't waste time looking for things. But I have a hard time starting a new project before my whole house is picked up and everything put away. I don't want to leave my home until it's ordered. This makes me late to appointments. It keeps me from focusing on important things. If I also value promptness, then I have an internal conflict. I choose to keep order on my list of values. It is important to me, but being aware of how this value can affect my life helps me to keep things in perspective.

Take a break from the travel guide to your life.

Go to a bookstore or library and find an official travel guide for the city or town where you live.

Write down three ideas of new places you could visit.

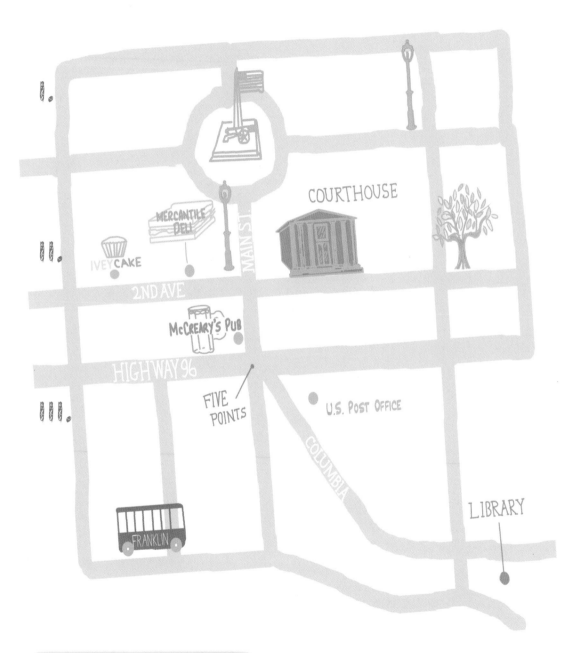

Creative Excursion: Find an open date on your calendar and make a plan to discover something new about your hometown.

It is important to distinguish between values,
goals and responsibilities. Taking care of my family is an
honorable responsibility, but when I lose sight of personal goals
or valuing my relationship with my husband,
the story of my life is incomplete.

values: What motivates you, what you treasure and hold dear,

your ethics

For example: people, especially friends and family-my faith-growth and
change-simplicity, comfort, and order.

goals: Your ambition, your objectives, your purpose

For example: to write-to run-to speak, to share my story, to encourage others-finish
my degree-to enjoy my kids-to be intimate and have fun with my husband

responsibilities: The actions necessary to achieve your

goals, duty, liability

For example: care of children: to provide an education, good nutrition, a safe, clean
and loving environment- commitment to my marriage, pursuing intimacy- manage my
home, money, meals, bills- personal growth: physical, mental and spiritual health

Jenny Black: Just because I value my friendships--and I deeply
value them--does not mean I should neglect my responsibilities.
Many peanutbutter and jelly sandwich dinners have resulted from
my choosing quality time with my friends over grocery shopping
and cooking. As hard as it is for me, sometimes, I have to choose my
chores over the things I really value. On the flip side, life would be
colorless if I woke up to responsibilities everyday without
the meaning relationships bring to me.

Assess your life to see if you have conflicting areas that are causing you frustration. No one can be everything to everyone, even to one's self, 100 percent of the time. Determine your own personal set of top values and make any adjustments you deem necessary.

values: What motivates you?

goals: What are your ambitions, your objectives?

responsibilities: What actions are necessary to achieve your goals?

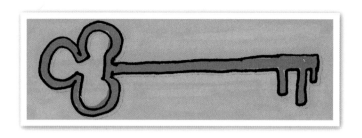

DO ANY OF YOUR VALUES GET IN THE WAY OF YOUR GOALS?

DOES IT STRESS YOU OUT TRYING TO KEEP YOUR GOALS, BECAUSE YOU NEVER GET TO THEM?

DO ANY OF YOUR VALUES CONFLICT?

AS YOU DIG DEEPER, DO YOU NEED TO MAKE ANY CHANGES TO YOUR LIST OF VALUES?

Jenny Watson: As a mother of young children, I valued serving my children – being the best mom I could be to them. I felt like a failure much of the time. Then I realized that the value I was holding was to be a "perfect" mother. I needed to redefine my values. In the beginning I tried to do something special for each of my children everyday. I could not keep up with my own expectations. Now I serve my children in a meaningful way once a week. This I can do. For my children who are in college, I try to do something for them once a month. My standards are now within my reach and my children feel valued.

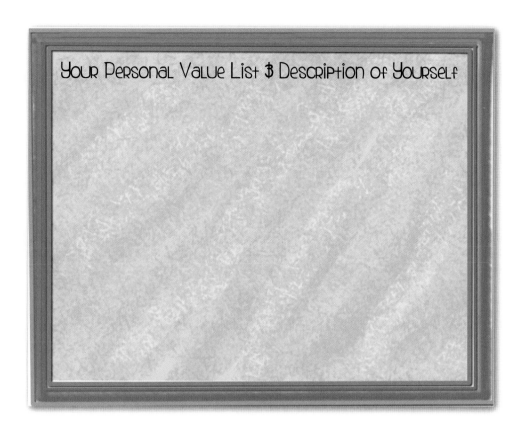

Your Personal Value List & Description of Yourself

DOES THIS DESCRIPTION SOUND LIKE YOU?

IN WHAT WAYS DOES YOUR LIFE REFLECT YOUR VALUES?

"Act as if you are and you will become such."
~Leo Tolstoy

Jenny Watson: Personal Value List & Description of Herself

1. Spirituality – Knowing and Pleasing God
2. Order
3. Warmth
4. Fun

This person enjoys being in relationship. She is in relationship with God and others. She enjoys people that stimulate her thinking and are stimulated by her. She needs to plan her fun activities so that she can keep order in her life and make sure that she has the resources needed. It may be hard for her to be spontaneous. She will make you feel good when you are with her.

Jenny Black: Personal Value List & Description of Herself.

1. Relationships
2. Faith/Spirituality
3. Space/Alone time
4. Simplicity, Comfort and Order

This person makes most of her decisions around getting to be with others. She is deeply spiritual and relates to people from her soul. She is often pulled between her need to be alone and her desire to be with her friends and family. Her priority of simplicity, comfort, and order is often compromised by her greater desire to connect in meaningful ways to others. She gets behind on household tasks and often has to do marathon cleanings to fulfill her need for order.

Road Trip:
Find a postcard or beautiful picture
of the place where you live.
You might use a picture from your creative excursion.

Write something important or interesting
about your city, town, or state:

Values are like Fingerprints. Each of us has our own unique set.

We don't expect anyone to have fingerprints that match ours, so why are we surprised when we discover we have different values? When we expect those who are on the journey with us to live by our set of rules, there is bound to be conflict.

Write down the names of some people you love. Next to their names write down the biggest conflict that you have with each person. Looking at your own values and examining them against the conflict, can you identify any rule that you are holding as a standard for this person? An opposing value may be the primary issue causing the conflict. What steps can you take to begin to respect his or her values?

*Name_____

Greatest Conflict(s)_____

Opposing Values_____

New Perspectives _____

*Name_____

Greatest Conflict(s)_____

Opposing Values_____

New Perspectives _____

*Name_____

Greatest Conflict(s)_____

Opposing Values_____

New Perspectives _____

Taking a *Wrong* Turn

What about the times when we go off course? Just because you may value warmth and kindness does not mean you always treat people with these values.

How do you recover when you don't follow your travel guide? Look over your personal value list. Think back on some times when you did not live in a way that was consistent with your values.

Describe the situations.

How did you feel?

"Goals are stars to steer by, not sticks to beat yourself with." — Barbara B. Smith

Your Favorite Mistake

What lessons have you learned from the mistakes you have made?

Jenny Black: Last year, my children were attending a community program where they were the new kids. The first day I was a few minutes late picking them up; I was the one everyone was waiting on. The volunteers were sitting there with my children, talking to them, reading to them, reviewing their experiences that day. I felt like one of those moms who has more important things to do than pick up her children. In the past, I would have felt inadequate and avoided the teachers for the rest of the week, hoping they would forget my tardiness. Instead, I bought them each a chocolate bar and wrote a note telling them how much I appreciated them. My minor mistake turned into an opportunity to make these women feel valued.

Road Trip: Make a list of recovery ideas.
Write it on a page in your to-do list for quick reference.

Taking the Law into Your Own Hands

Your values are the laws that you choose to live by.
Using your personal value list, what laws would you create
for your world?

A new law for myself –

A new law for my household –

A new law for my neighborhood –

A new law for my employer or school –

A new law for my country –

A new law for the whole wide world –

After looking at the laws you would impose if given the opportunity…What did you learn about yourself?

Do you think that you are imposing some of your values unfairly on others?

On yourself?

Jenny Watson: After a recent tragedy where a young woman lost her life, I was struck by a reporter's description of the victim. She said, "The girl loved to play lacrosse, eat Italian food and loved the color blue." This description seemed so incomplete. Surely this was not all her life amounted to. Didn't anyone know what was really important to her? What she was passionate about? I love that I know what I love. I love that I include these things in my life. This makes my life so rewarding, pleasurable and fun, but those things are not how I want to be remembered.

Think about how you would like to be remembered.

What words would you like to be spoken about you if you were no longer here?

If this is how you want to be remembered at the end of your life, is anything keeping you from living this way now?

Our Souvenirs

Jenny Black: I know who I want to be. I know what I want people to see in me. But I am still more concerned with not stepping on anyone's toes than I am living the passionate life for which I was created. I am a warrior inside. Most people only see the nice girl because I am still protecting myself from being rejected. Do I want to be liked or do I want to live fully? This chapter helped me to clarify and define my life values. They were already inside of me, but I had not put words to them. Now I have to decide if I am going to be true to my values. This is not as simple as just deciding to change. It is a journey taken one day at a time.

Jenny Watson: Wow! I know I have to live in a way that is consistent with my personal values to be fulfilled. I expect others to allow me to do what I need to do to live this way, but I have not given them the freedom to do the same. When someone in my family pursues their hobby or goes to the swimming pool when there is much to be done in our home, I judge them. I take it personally that they aren't planning their day around what I perceive to be the priority. Just as you can only control your own behavior, you can only hold **yourself** responsible to live according to your values. Thankfully I have many friends with similar values who encourage me to be true to myself. Thankfully I have chosen a spouse who respects my values. If I love them, then I will embrace their personal values and will encourage them to live a consistent life as well.

Your Souvenirs

-respect for your values and for other people's values

-the ability to distinguish what you really value from what you think you should value

-no longer being afraid of making mistakes; instead, anticipating your recovery

Chapter Five

A Walk Down Memory Lane

embracing your past

walk

verb, noun.
v.i. **1.** to go on foot.
In walking, a person always has one
foot on the ground.
2. to roam.
3. to go slowly.

memory

noun, pl. **-ries.**
1. the ability to remember or
keep in the mind;
capacity to retain or recall that which
is learned or experienced.
2. the act or fact of
remembering; remembrance;
recollection.
3. a person, thing, or event that
is remembered.
4. all that a person remembers;
what can be recalled to mind.
5. the length of past time that is
remembered.

lane

noun.
1. a narrow way between
hedges, walls, or fences,
especially a narrow country road or
path or city street.

A slow, thoughtful walk down

Memory Lane...

You cannot rush through this part of the journey.

Neither can you live here forever.

Your past does not define you, but it is where
your story begins. Every family is made up of
people passing on to their children what they know
about life~ usually hoping to do better than the
generation before them.

A Walk down Memory Lane is about...

Grace

Appreciation

Resilience

and

Redemption

Grab your personal favorite childhood snack
and meet us on the front porch
of your childhood home.

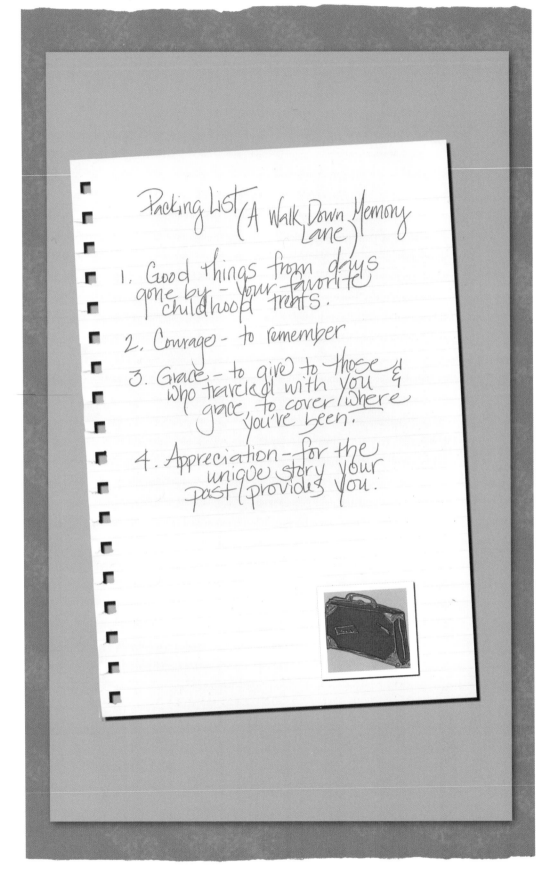

Packing List (A Walk Down Memory Lane)

1. Good things from days gone by – your favorite childhood treats.

2. Courage – to remember

3. Grace – to give to those who traveled with you & grace, to cover where you've been.

4. Appreciation – for the unique story your past provides you.

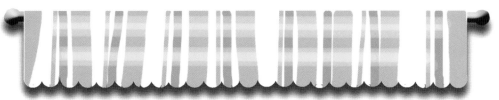

WHen you Read the title of this chapter, what feelings immediately surfaced?

Did you think of warm cookies baking in the oven or an empty house where you don't feel welcome?

Most likely, when we ask you to embrace your past,
you are having a polar reaction…
you either hate us (for suggesting such a painful journey) or you think,
*This will be easy—I had the perfect childhood. My parents did it all right
(or tried to) and this chapter will be a breeze for me.*

If you try to get through life without an appreciation for the entire
experience of your past, you will not only stop your own growth,
you will pass on the same story to the generations that come after you.
Your past is affecting your life today, whether or not you acknowledge it.

List the names of these family members and briefly describe your relationship with them:

My parents or guardians:

My grandparents:

My siblings or cousins:

My aunts or uncles:

Road Trip: Find a picture of yourself in the following stages and write about what you see.

My CHILdHOOd

My Teen Years

Describe your role in your family.
(Rescuer-Comedian-Caretaker-Baby-Leader)

It is in our family that we develop patterns for how we relate to others in the real world.

Do you still play the same role in your life today?

In what ways has your role changed in your adult life?

In what ways would you like your role to change?

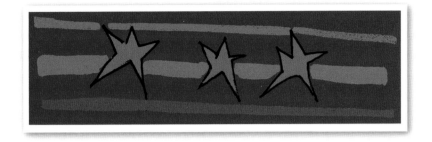

Proudest moment with my family:

Most humiliating moment with my family:

Greatest conversation I ever had with a family member:

Most painful conversation I ever had with a family member:

Are you *too close* *or* too distant *to any one of your family members?*

To whom would you like to be closer?

From whom would you like a bit more distance?

What steps could you take toward more balance in these relationships?

We get into ruts in how we connect with our families. Try to think of some new ways you could connect, especially if your relationship is based on talking about someone else.
Think about getting to know your family as if you were a stranger. You will be surprised at the things you learn.

Road Trip: Make a date with a family member you would like to get to know better.

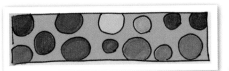

Creative Excursion: If your life story was made into a movie, what songs would be on your soundtrack?

Song Title	Artist	Album	Genre

Describe your role and any **teachers** or *friends* you had or still have from these times in your life.

Elementary:

Middle:

High:

College:

Beyond:

Jenny Black: Over Christmas break, my best friends from high school went through boxes of notes we passed each other in class. We laughed and cried over all of our drama. It was a wonderful reminder of how much we have changed and how much we have remained exactly the same.

Find a note or significant letter from your past and tape it on this page:

Road Trip: Contact an old friend with whom you have lost touch. Send a letter to someone who made a difference in your life.

What *life lessons* have you learned from:

Your Mom:

Your Dad:

Friends:

Teachers:

Co-workers:

Describe three moments of *pure joy* from your past.

1.

2.

3.

Road Trip: Write a few words that will remind you of these moments and keep them on your refrigerator or bathroom mirror. Remembering these moments can bring you to a place of appreciation when times get tough, relationships get strained, or even in times of loss and grief.

Our Souvenirs

Jenny Black: "Mom, I need to tell you about something that hurt my feelings." I love that I have this kind of openness with my daughter and I was hoping to put her heart at ease. "About what, Avery?" "Well, you told someone the other day that when we were playing with our friends, you were able to get a lot of stuff done that you can't usually do when we are around. That made me feel like you don't want to be around us." After assuring her that I enjoy her company, I explained how challenging some of the responsibilities are of being a parent. I told her about a similar situation with my mother when I was younger. My mom was telling a friend how nice it would be to have a break from the kids. It hurt my feelings. I wondered if she thought we were awful to be around. When I told Avery how my feelings had been hurt just like hers, she asked if I had ever talked to my mom about that story. When I said it never occurred to me to tell her about it, she insisted the next time I see her, I tell her how much that hurt my feelings. After several rare minutes of silence from my son, he piped in, "Well, it's sort of too late now." That got me laughing so hard I could not respond. "Well, it's true," he continued, "What is she gonna do about it now?" Both of my kids made great points. While writing these chapters, I discovered how important it is to find the balance between these two perspectives. As Brandon pointed out, my mom can't do anything about hurting my feelings when I was a six-year-old. (And I fully understand needing a break from the kids.) But Avery had a great point, too. Last weekend I told my mom the story and she teared up. "We didn't know how to talk to each other that way when you kids were little," she said. "Isn't it great that you guys do?" I am lucky to still have my parents with me. My dad has already lost his parents. Our true regrets will not be what others have done to us, but how we treated them. Today brings a precious opportunity to continue growing in my relationship with my family.

Jenny Watson: This was the most personal and deepest section of this book for me. Working through it was paralyzing in some ways. Some people do not feel like this, but I find it interesting to examine myself. It is hard to take a look at relationships and how we have influenced each other. I can't control others and make them respond in the way I want them to. I still struggle with resentment, but now I know that to be whole I have to let others off the hook. This is a process I am embracing. I also see how things from my past have given me the ability and strength to do what I feel called to do today. I never want to be the cause for hurt in someone's life. My parents did not want to do that either, but there are hurts. I cause them also. Some of the very things that hurt me, I do to others. The significance of "The Golden Rule" has never been clearer. The legacy that I want to pass on from here includes doing some things differently, but most importantly, I want to pass on a legacy of acceptance and forgiveness. Today will soon be a walk down memory lane for my children.

Your Souvenirs

~An authentic understanding of how far you've come

~New ways to relate to your family

CHAPTER SIX

Coming Home
living beyond yourself

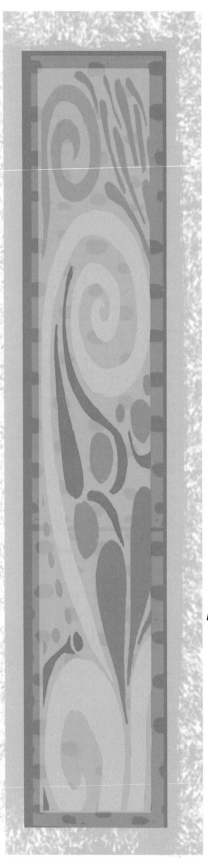

coming

noun, adjective.

noun **1.** a drawing near; approach; arrival.
Ex. the coming of summer.
(SYN) advent.
2. Often, **Coming.** Christ's Second Advent.
adj. **1.** approaching; next.
Ex. He plans to travel to Europe this coming summer.
(SYN) forthcoming, impending.
2. (Informal.) on the way to importance or fame.
Ex. He is a coming politician.
(SYN) promising.

home

noun, adjective, adverb, verb,

homed, homing.
noun **1.** the place where a person or family lives;
one's own house or dwelling place.
(SYN) residence, dwelling, abode.

The drive home is the longest part of any journey.
Slowly the realities of your real life
start creeping back to the top of your mind.
You walk into the front door.
In spite of the piles of bills, dirty clothes,
emails and phone calls
demanding your immediate attention,
you think to yourself,
"It is good to be home".

You have been on quite an excursion.
You took a honeymoon and
a sightseeing trip.
You searched your soul,
consulted your travel guide
and took a walk down memory lane.

Now you are coming home.

You have your souvenirs.
As you unpack them,
do you wish you were still on your honeymoon?
Are you prepared to meet the demands of daily life?
Hopefully, you know yourself better today
than you did at the beginning of our journey.
You might even have a clearer picture
of who you want to be
and what you want your life to be about.

It is our hope that coming home
is your greatest adventure yet!!

"Un" packing List
(for Coming Home)

(1) This book- to plan how to incorporate new things into your life.

(2) Dirty Laundry- Wash it, burn it... You know you'll have it!

(3) Gifts (Souvenirs) - Things you've gathered on your journey to give away.

(4) Appointment book / Calendar - to schedule a date to share your travel stories.

(5) Patience - for yourself & for others.

YOUR HABITAT

Home stays the same even though you have changed. Maybe you discovered your *favorite color* or a *new style* that is you, but your home reflects someone you thought you were or someone you were trying to be. This is what **Coming Home** is all about.

If you have learned to incorporate new things into your life, if you have learned to *respond* in new ways, the thing to keep in mind is NEW. Home is where you lived when you were living in your old patterns.

How do we take all that we have learned and incorporate it into real LIFE? How do we personalize our lives in our current surroundings?

Remember when you discovered that different animals require different habitats? We are no different. Each of us has a specific environment in which we thrive. Look back at the "What I know now" pages from each chapter.

What are the things you have learned that you need in your habitat to really thrive? It may be a favorite thing from Chapter One.

If coming home for you feels like you are caged in a zoo for the enjoyment of other people, what things can change?

What things can't change? How can you change in response to them?

What can you not live without?

How will you incorporate these things? List specifics.

What positive changes have you seen in your home since you began to write this book?

Sharing Your Travels

With whom would you most like to share your journey? Don't be disappointed if someone you are close to doesn't understand fully the new insights you have gained. Find some people who are interested in introspection and share with them. Select your three favorite questions from each chapter. Write down at least one person with whom you would like to discuss these.

Chapter 1 – Your Honeymoon

1.

2.

3.

Chapter 2 – Sightseeing

1.

2.

3.

Chapter 3 – Soul~Searching

1.

2.

3.

Chapter 4 – Your Travel Guide

1.

2.

3.

Chapter 5 – A Walk down Memory Lane

1.

2.

3.

You know yourself on a much deeper level. What are you doing with what you have learned?

Life is full of circumstances that are challenging. Recognize what aspects of your "habitat" are equipping and stretching you and which ones are keeping you from thriving. Do not confuse a difficult situation with an impossible one. Everything that is truly valuable to us has cost us more time, more money, more emotion, and more energy than we could ever imagine possessing. And yet as we look at our marriages, our children, our careers, and our future, we realize nothing of true worth comes easily.

We often make huge life choices based on old voices. Many are on this journey because suddenly their life doesn't match what they value anymore. We cannot simply drop all of our responsibilities and relationships just because we can no longer live up to the standards we set for ourselves. If you are ready to run away from home, take a time out. You need space. You need time, but you also need relationships.

How do you stay connected with the others in your life who are not on the same journey?

 *Road Trip*: make a date with someone special to you and share what you have learned from your travels in this book.

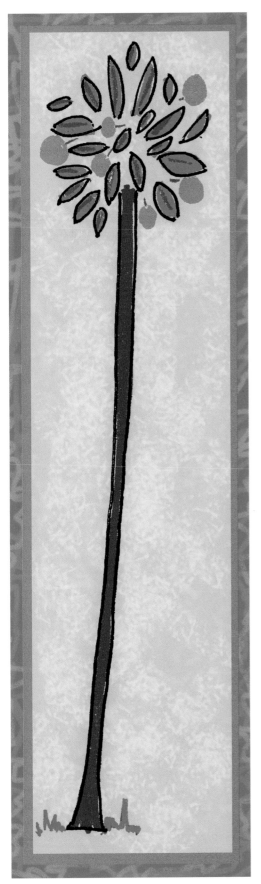

What have been the greatest
conflicts or resistors to change?

What can you do about this?

Is there a compromise to be made,
or is this a process
with which you need to be patient?

Taking care of yourself is not the same as being selfish.

selfish, *adjective.*

    1. caring too much for oneself and too little for others. A selfish person puts his own interests first.

    2. showing care solely or chiefly for oneself.

Based on the above definition, what could possibly be good about being selfish? Have you ever met people who lived their entire lives caring more about themselves than others? I have known some people like that, and when they died, the ones who loved them did not grieve their death, but their life, and what it was missing. A selfish life is a lonely life.

Do not confuse taking care of yourself with being selfish.

You have needs. We have needs. Take care of the needs, if possible. If you feel like you are about to go off the deep end (or even if you already have) tell someone, pray, laugh, scream, write about it. Eat chocolate. Take a bath.

We love when women take care of themselves.

We must take care of ourselves because there are others who cannot. We have to fight for those who have less power than we do. Those promises that are written on your heart, from the Soul~Searching chapter, are not simply there for you to live a more fulfilled life. They are there because you have been given things that others have not been given. You have a responsibility to believe and live out those promises because your life could change someone else's world.

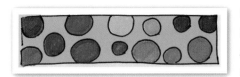

Creative Excursion*: *Make a date to take care of yourself this week. Do something wonderful and luxurious and don't feel an ounce of guilt for it.*

Write about your plans:

*Also put on your calendar a way you could serve someone else this week. If your life requires a high level of service already, make note of it and give yourself to that job with joy.

Who are some people who have changed your life? Think not only about your lifetime, but heroes from the past who fought for your freedom. Have you watched a movie or read a book that made you think, *I want to do something that great*?

Who are your heroes and what do you respect about them?

In your family:

In history:

In the world around you:

How do you want to live your life in a way similar to theirs?

Road Trip: Do some research through interviews or books. Learn about your hero's struggles, insecurities, and greatest strengths.

Happy New Day!

If you had to make New Year's Resolutions right now,
what would yours be?

Physical:

Mental:

Spiritual:

Emotional:

Social:

Intellectual:

Relational:

You must communicate who you are

and what you have learned

to the others in your life.

Since you are the one who has changed,

don't expect everyone else to read your mind.

Find small ways to remain true to yourself:

*Start something new.

*Balance these new insights with the

responsibilities that belong to you.

*Create a writing group with others who are

interested in sharing their journeys with you.

* As

you

face

new

struggles or old challenges, go back to the

Soul-Searching chapter and see what your

spirit

has to say to you.

* Ask for help.

* Ask for prayer.

* Ask for guidance.

* Let go of guilt.

* Enjoy your life.

Our Souvenirs

Jenny Black: Filling these pages with my very own story, my very own longings, helped me realize that it is ALL important! Having my walls painted my new favorite color (it is white!) speaks simplicity to me. It helps me to breathe deeply and gives my overstimulated mind a rest. Doing housework is very unsatisfying to me. But having an uncluttered and organized living space makes room in my life for the creative things I love. For a season of my life, I set aside becoming a person to take care of other people. Eventually I was tired and bitter. Reacting from a place of hurt, I started taking care of myself and I pushed others away. These travels led me on a journey of embracing it all, valuing the big and small things, myself and others, with dignity. When we began writing this journal, I also began opening myself to the promises of my life. From this I have had several travel opportunities, some with my husband some with my kids. My family has purchased a lake house right next to the tiny house where we first began cutting and pasting the honeymoon chapter. I now have my very own honeymoon suite! There is power in the words you write on these pages.

"Be careful what you set your heart upon for it will surely be yours."
~ James A. Baldwin

Jenny Watson: Journeying through this book, my dreams for my life and for my future have been clarified. Now I evaluate my current situation in response to what I have discovered. I find myself asking questions, *Does my environment reflect my dreams? Do my activities?* The answers motivate me to make the changes that are within my control. I am still in process regarding some things~ like allowing others to live out their own values. This is not something that I will immediately perfect, but something that will change my home and will affect the legacy that I leave. Knowing who I am and what I need adds to my home and to my life. I thought knowing myself was selfish, that took from others and gave to me. Now I know that there are things that are mine to give and ignoring them is what steals from others. Sure, all the daily chores of life are here too. But I hope that growth continues and when I don't feel like making dinner, I'll see all of my options: I can call in pizza or I can try out a new meatloaf recipe. I vow to annually review my Souvenirs.

"Go to your bosom, knock there and ask your heart what it doth know."
~William Shakespeare

Your Souvenirs

~Giving of yourself without giving yourself away
~Enjoyment of whatever life has for you today
~Appreciation for the people in your life

Your

Un.writ.ten Tra.vel(s)

are now complete.
You have turned the page
on the final chapter of this book.
We are honored that you have taken
this journey with us.
We'd love to take a road trip with
you into your life. Our journey will be
enriched by sharing in yours.

Send us feedback at
unwrittentravels.com